...icture?

...away.

...g away

...?

Snake is Going Away!

Where is Snake going?

Walkthrough

This is the back cover.

This is the blurb.

Let's read the blurb together.

'Where is Snake going?'

Snake is Going Away!

Alison Hawes
Illustrated by Charlotte Combe

Walkthrough

Look at the picture on the title page and tell me what you see (*case, sunglasses, surfboard*).

Where do you think Snake is going?

These are the names of the author and illustrator.

This is the publisher's logo.

Walkthrough

What do you think Snake says to Hippo?

Point out the speech marks.

How do you think Hippo feels?

"I am going away,"
said Snake.

👁 Observe and Prompt

Word Recognition

- If the children have difficulty with the word 'going', ask them if they recognise the initial letter and sound – 'g'. Then tell them the word and model the reading of it for them.

- The words 'away' and 'Snake' may not be decodable for the children at this stage. Tell them these words and model the reading of them.

2

Language Comprehension

- Observe reading with expression.
- Ask the children what Snake is saying.
- Where do the children think he might be going?

3

Walkthrough

Hippo thinks Snake is going away for a long time.

What might he tell Giraffe?

Is 'for ever' a long time?

"Look!" said Hippo.
"Snake is going away for ever!"

 Observe and Prompt

Word Recognition

- Check the children are using their decoding skills to read the words 'look' and 'Hippo'. Encourage them to blend the sounds through the words.

- Check the children can read 'said' and 'is'. (These are sight words – words likely to be in their store of familiar words.)

- You may want to help the children read the words 'for' and 'ever'.

Snake's House

5

👁 Observe and Prompt

Language Comprehension

- Ask the children what Hippo is saying.
- How do the children think Hippo might feel?
- How long does Hippo say Snake is going away for?

What do you think Giraffe tells Monkey?

How do you think Giraffe and Hippo feel?

What is Snake doing?

"Look!" said Giraffe.
"Snake is going away for ever!"

 Observe and Prompt

Word Recognition

- The word 'Giraffe' will not be decodable for the children at this stage. Tell the children this word and model the reading of it for them.

- Check the children can read the sight words 'said' and 'is' with confidence.

👁 Observe and Prompt

Language Comprehension

- Prompt for reading with expression.
- Ask the children who is talking now.
- Ask the children who they think the main character in this story is.

Walkthrough

What do you think Monkey says?

What is Snake doing now?

What do you think the animals will do?

"Look!" said Monkey.
"Snake is going away for ever!"

 Observe and Prompt

Word Recognition

- If the children have difficulty with the word 'monkey', ask them if they recognise the initial letter and sound – 'm'. Then tell them the word and model the reading of it for them.

Snake's House

9

Observe and Prompt

Language Comprehension

- Check the children understand what is happening now.
- Ask the children what Monkey says.
- How do the children think Monkey feels?

Walkthrough

Do they want Snake to go away for ever?

What might Monkey say to Snake?

How do you think Snake looks? (*surprised*)

"Don't go away for ever, Snake!" said Monkey.

10

 Observe and Prompt

Word Recognition

- The word 'don't' may not be fully decodable for the children at this stage. If they have difficulty, ask them if they recognise the initial letter and sound – 'd'. Then model the reading of this word for them.
- Check children can read 'go' – a sight word.

Snake's House

11

 Observe and Prompt

Language Comprehension

- Ask the children what Monkey says now.
- Check the children understand who Monkey is talking to.
- Why do the children think Monkey does not want Snake to go?

Walkthrough

Is Snake going away for ever?

What might he tell his friends?

Why do his friends look surprised?

What's happening in the picture?

"I'm not going away for ever," said Snake.

Observe and Prompt

Word Recognition

- Check the children can read 'I'm'. Point out the apostrophe.
- Check children are reading the CVC word 'not' using their decoding skills. Can they sound out and blend n-o-t all through the word?

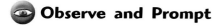

👁 Observe and Prompt

Language Comprehension

- Prompt for reading with expression.
- Check the children understand what is happening now in the story.
- Ask the children what Snake says.

Walkthrough

Where do you think Snake is going?

Where might the taxi be taking Snake?

"I'm going away on holiday!"

 Observe and Prompt

Word Recognition

- If the children have difficulty with the word 'holiday', ask them if they recognise the initial letter and sound – 'h'. Then prompt them to blend the sounds from left to right through the word.

15

👁 Observe and Prompt

Language Comprehension

- Ask the children what is happening now in the story.
- How do the children think the animals feel now?
- What do the children think might happen next in the story?

Walkthrough

What might Snake say? (Point out speech bubbles.)

When do you think Snake will see his friends?

 Observe and Prompt

Word Recognition

- Check the children are using their decoding skills to read 'see' and 'soon'. Can they blend the sounds through these words?
- Check the children can read the sight word 'you'.

Language Comprehension

- Check the children understand what happened at the end of the story.
- Ask the children where Snake has gone. When will he be back?
- Ask the children who the main character in this story was.